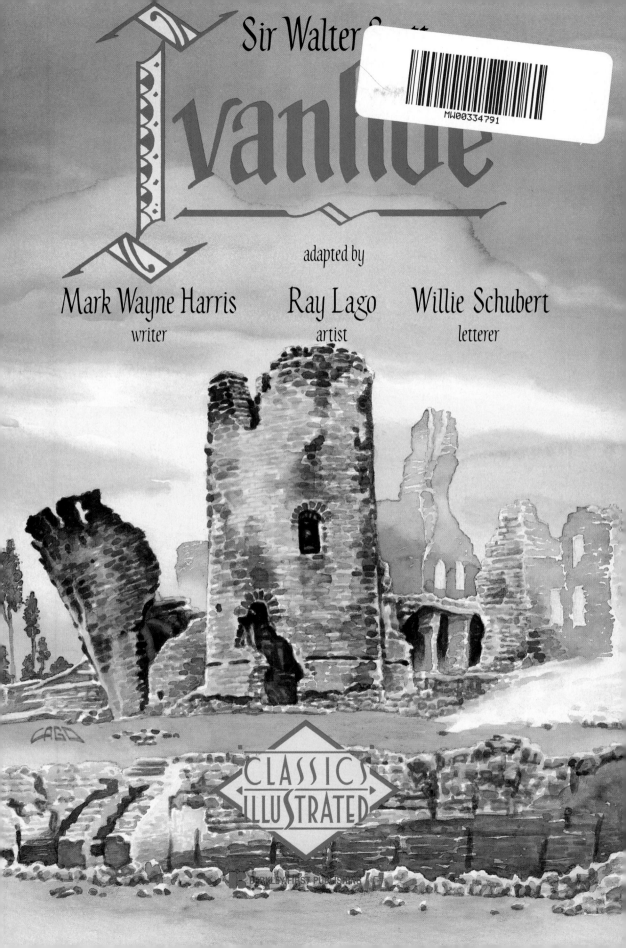

Sir Walter Scott

Ivanhoe

adapted by

Mark Wayne Harris
writer

Ray Lago
artist

Willie Schubert
letterer

CLASSICS
ILLUSTRATED

BERKLEY/FIRST PUBLISHING

Ivanhoe was Sir Walter Scott's most popular novel, set in a twelfth-century England that brimmed with adventure, romance and chivalry. When **Ivanhoe** was published in 1820, Scott already was a major cultural force, considered the architect of the historical novel and the short story. With novels such as *Tales of My Landlord* (1816-19) and *Rob Roy* (1817), he helped shape the English romantic movement; his characters, meanwhile, served as models for the reserved gentlefolks that typified the Victorian gentry. **Ivanhoe** demonstrates Scott's ambivalence about the Middle Ages and its code of honor: while he was enamored of the period's romance and grandeur, Scott was disturbed by what he saw as chivalry's excesses. That conflict — between the majestic pomp and the decadence of the law of the land— lies at the novel's heart. Scott uses his characters to pass judgment on the inhumanity, reckless abandonment, and vainglorious behavior common under the chivalric code. Indeed, the novel's practical heroine, Rebecca, remarks that chivalry is only "heroic folly." Scott's wedding of historical fact, romantic fiction, and social concern not only entertained, but challenged the imagination; his work inspired a critical reassessment of England's past, and an intelligent examination of its current social values. Generations later, Scott's stories continue to provoke thought. As an example, readers throughout the years have questioned why it is Rowena, rather than the good-hearted, patient Rebecca, who wins Ivanhoe's hand. One reason is philosophical: Scott felt that Rebecca's unbending stoicism should not be rewarded by obvious gratification, an outcome he believed would demean her bountiful faith. The other reason is social: Scott claimed correctly that religious prejudice during the Middle Ages would have prevented the Jewish heroine and the Christian hero from wedding. It is a sad reality, one made more bitter by the reader's sympathy for the unselfish, gracious Jewess. In **Ivanhoe**, Scott's attentiveness to details — including unfortunate realities, many of which are still with us — combine with his sense of romance and adventure to produce a thrilling tale, one that provides not only a look inside life in medieval England, but a glimpse inside life today.

Ivanhoe
Classics Illustrated, Number 25

Wade Roberts, Editorial Director   Kurt Goldzung, Creative Director
Mike McCormick, Art Director   Valarie Jones, Editor

PRINTING HISTORY
1st edition published May 1991

For information, address: First Publishing, Inc., 435 North LaSalle St., Chicago, Illinois 60610.

ISBN 0-425-12526-2

Distributed by Berkley Sales & Marketing, a division of The Berkley Publishing Group, 200 Madison Avenue, New York, New York 10016.

Printed in the United States of America
1 2 3 4 5 6 7 8 9 0

1 N THAT PLEASANT DISTRICT OF MERRY ENGLAND WHICH IS WATERED BY THE RIVER DON, THERE EXTENDED IN ANCIENT TIMES A LARGE FOREST, COVERING THE GREATER PART OF THE BEAUTIFUL HILLS AND VALLEYS WHICH LIE BETWEEN SHEFFIELD AND THE PLEASANT TOWN OF DONCASTER...

"FANGS! HERE, FANGS!"

A DEVIL CONFOUND THE RANGER THAT CUTS THE CLAWS OFF OUR DOGS, AND MAKES THEM UNFIT FOR THEIR TRADE.

WAMBA, UP AND HELP ME.

I ADVISE THEE TO LEAVE THE HERD TO THEIR DESTINY, GURTH, WHICH CAN BE LITTLE ELSE THAN TO BE CONVERTED INTO NORMANS BEFORE MORNING.

TURNED NORMANS? EXPOUND THAT, FOR MY MIND IS TOO DULL TO READ RIDDLES.

WHY, GURTH, HOW CALL YOU THESE BRUTES RUNNING ABOUT ON THEIR FOUR LEGS?

SWINE, FOOL-- SWINE. EVERY FOOL KNOWS THAT.

PORK.

AND PORK IS GOOD NORMAN-FRENCH. SO WHEN THE BRUTE LIVES, AND IS IN THE CHARGE OF A SAXON SLAVE, SHE GOES BY HER SAXON NAME--

IT IS BUT TOO TRUE DOCTRINE, HOWEVER IT GOT INTO THY FOOL'S PATE.

I CAN TELL YOU MORE--BUT SOFT, WHOM HAVE WE HERE?

AND SWINE IS GOOD SAXON. BUT HOW CALL YOU WHEN SHE IS FLAYED, DRAWN, QUARTERED AND HUNG UP BY THE HEELS?

--BUT BECOMES A NORMAN AND CALLED PORK WHEN CARRIED TO FEAST AMONG THE NOBLES.

WHAT DOST THOU THINK OF THIS, FRIEND GURTH--HA?

THE STRANGER WAS ACCOMMODATED, AND AT LENGTH HE ANNOUNCED ROTHERWOOD, THE DWELLING OF CEDRIC THE SAXON.

FINDING HIMSELF NOW NEAR SHELTER, PRIOR AYMER'S CURIOSITY BEGAN TO AWAKE, AND HE DEMANDED OF THE GUIDE WHO AND WHAT HE WAS.

THE STRANGER REPORTED THAT HE WAS A PALMER, A PILGRIM JUST RETURNED FROM THE HOLY LAND, AND A NATIVE OF THE PARTS.

ALL WERE SOON SEATED IN A HALL PREPARED FOR THE EVENING MEAL OF CEDRIC THE SAXON, AN UNWILLING BUT COURTEOUS HOST.

THEY WERE JOINED BY CEDRIC'S WARD, ROWENA. HER BEAUTY WAS NOT LOST ON BOIS-GUILBERT...

...WHOSE INTEREST WAS, IN TURN, NOT LOST ON CEDRIC, WHO TURNED THE SUBJECT OF CONVERSATION TO THE CRUSADES.

TELL ME, SIR BRIAN--WHO BEAR THEMSELVES BEST IN PALESTINE?

THE NORMAN KNIGHTS TEMPLAR, WHO ARE SWORN TO CHAMPION THE HOLY CROSS.

WERE THERE, THEN, NONE AMONG THE SAXONS WHOSE NAMES ARE WORTHY TO BE MENTIONED?

FORGIVE ME, LADY...

...THE ENGLISH WERE SECOND *ONLY* TO THE KNIGHTS OF THE TEMPLE.

THEY WERE SECOND TO *NONE*.

I MYSELF SAW THEE, SIR TEMPLAR, CAST TO THE GROUND BY A SAXON KNIGHT IN THE TOURNEY AT ST. JOHN-DE-ACRE.

THE VICTOR WAS A YOUNG KNIGHT OF LESSER RENOWN. HIS NAME DWELLS NOT IN MY MEMORY.

I WILL MYSELF NAME THE ONE BEFORE WHOSE LANCE FORTUNE--AND MY HORSE'S FAULT--CAUSED MY FALL.

IT WAS THE KNIGHT OF IVANHOE.

AND WERE HE IN ENGLAND, I--MOUNTED AND ARMED AS I NOW AM--WOULD GIVE HIM EVERY ADVANTAGE OF WEAPONS AND ABIDE THE RESULT.

YOUR CHALLENGE WOULD SOON BE ANSWERED...

...WERE YOUR ANTAGONIST NEAR YOU.

IF IVANHOE RETURNS FROM PALESTINE, I WILL BE HIS SURETY THAT HE MEETS YOU.

IF HE DOES NOT I WILL PROCLAIM HIM A COWARD ON THE WALLS OF EVERY TEMPLE COURT IN EUROPE.

MASTER, A JEW WHO CALLS HIMSELF ISAAC OF YORK SEEKS ADMITTANCE AND HOSPITALITY.

LET HIS WANTS BE ADMINISTERED TO WITH ALL CARE, OSWALD.

A JEW...TO APPROACH A DEFENDER OF THE HOLY SEPULCHRE?

ST. MARY! AN UNBELIEVING JEW ADMITTED INTO THIS PRESENCE!

PEACE, MY WORTHY GUESTS. MY HOSPITALITY MUST NOT BE BOUNDED BY YOUR DISLIKES.

4

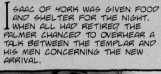

ISAAC OF YORK WAS GIVEN FOOD AND SHELTER FOR THE NIGHT. WHEN ALL HAD RETIRED, THE PALMER CHANCED TO OVERHEAR A TALK BETWEEN THE TEMPLAR AND HIS MEN CONCERNING THE NEW ARRIVAL.

AT DAWN'S FIRST LIGHT, THE PALMER ENTERED THE JEW'S ROOM...

...AND ROUSED HIM FROM A FITFUL SLUMBER.

FEAR NOTHING FROM ME, ISAAC. I COME AS A FRIEND TO TELL YOU THE TEMPLAR PLANS TO ABDUCT YOU FOR RANSOM AND TAKE YOU TO THE CASTLE OF REGINALD FRONT-DE-BOEUF.

HOLY GOD OF ABRAHAM!

I WILL POINT OUT THE MEANS OF YOUR ESCAPE, AND GUIDE YOU THROUGH THE SECRET PATHS OF THE FOREST.

I WILL NOT LEAVE YOU UNTIL YOU ARE SAFE.

THEY ENTERED THE CELL OF GURTH. THE PALMER WHISPERED IN THE SWINEHERD'S EAR. GURTH STARTED UP AS IF ELECTRIFIED.

GURTH, BEWARE-- THOU ART WONT TO BE PRUDENT. UNDO THE POSTERN GATE AND LET OUT THE JEW AND ME.

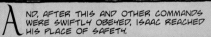

AND, AFTER THIS AND OTHER COMMANDS WERE SWIFTLY OBEYED, ISAAC REACHED HIS PLACE OF SAFETY.

THE BLESSINGS OF JACOB UPON YOU, GOOD YOUTH! YOU HAVE SAID YOU DESIRE NO RECOMPENSE...

YET, I CAN TELL THEE THY WISH-- A HORSE AND ARMOR FOR THE UPCOMING TOURNAMENT.

WHAT FIEND PROMPTED *THAT* GUESS?

IN THE BOSOM OF THAT PALMER'S GOWN IS HIDDEN A KNIGHT'S CHAIN AND SPURS. THEY GLANCED AS YOU STOOPED OVER MY BED.

TAKE THIS TO MY KINSMAN IN LEICESTER. HE WILL FURNISH THEE WITH THY CHOICE-- YOU HAVE ONLY TO RETURN THEM WHEN THE TOURNEY IS OVER.

THE FIRST DAY OF THE TOURNAMENT AT ASHBY-DE-LA-ZOUCHE. IN ITS STANDS WERE:

PRINCE JOHN, RULER OF ENGLAND IN KING RICHARD'S ABSENCE...

...WALDEMAR FITZURSE, COUNSELOR TO THE PRINCE...

...ISAAC OF YORK AND HIS BEAUTIFUL DAUGHTER REBECCA...

...CEDRIC AND ROWENA...

CEDRIC HAD PLEDGED ROWENA TO MARRY ATHELSTANE, THOUGH HER HEART BELONGED TO HIS OWN SON, WILFRED OF IVANHOE, WHOM CEDRIC HAD BANISHED FOR LOOKING UPON HER WITH LOVE.

...AND ATHELSTANE, DESCENDANT OF THE LAST SAXON KING.

FIVE NORMANS LED BY BOIS-GUILBERT CHALLENGED ALL COMERS. THOSE WHO ACCEPTED, ALL SAXONS, WERE BRUTALLY DEFEATED AGAIN AND AGAIN.

BUT NONE SHARED THE FEELING OF DEFEAT AS KEENLY AS CEDRIC, WHO SAW EACH NORMAN VICTORY AS A TRIUMPH OVER THE HONOR OF ENGLAND.

SIR DISINHERITED KNIGHT IT IS NOW YOUR DUTY TO NAME THE QUEEN OF LOVE AND BEAUTY WHO IS TO PRESIDE OVER NEXT DAY'S FESTIVAL.

THE DISINHERITED KNIGHT RODE SWIFTLY AROUND THE LISTS, AND AT LENGTH PAUSED BEFORE THE LADY ROWENA.

THE SPECTATORS APPLAUDED HIS CHOICE.

THE CHAMPION RETIRED TO HIS TENT, WHERE HE WAS VISITED BY FIVE SQUIRES OF HIS DEFEATED CHALLENGERS.

EACH OFFERED, ACCORDING TO THE LAWS OF CHIVALRY, HIS CHOICE OF THEIR MASTER'S ARMS AND ARMOR, OR AN EQUIVALENT RANSOM.

HE ACCEPTED A RANSOM FROM EACH--EXCEPT THE SQUIRE OF BOIS-GUILBERT.

TELL YOUR MASTER, IN MY NAME THAT OUR STRIFE IS NOT ENDED.

NOT TILL WE HAVE FOUGHT AS WELL WITH SWORDS AS WITH LANCES, AS WELL ON FOOT AS ON HORSEBACK.

RESTORE THE HORSE AND ARMOR TO THY MASTER. IF HE SCORNS TO ACCEPT THEM, RETAIN THEM FOR THINE OWN USE.

9

REBECCA THEN APPEARED AND GAVE GURTH ONE HUNDRED ZECCHINS TO RESTORE TO HIS MASTER, SAYING HER FATHER OWED HIM A DEEPER KINDNESS THAN MONEY COULD REPAY. GURTH THANKED HER AND BEGAN HIS JOURNEY HOME.

THE CHAMPION THEN SENT GURTH TO ASHBY TO REPAY ISAAC EIGHTY ZECCHINS FOR HIS KINDNESS. ISAAC ACCEPTED THESE AND GURTH TOOK HIS LEAVE.

HIS NOCTURNAL ADVENTURES, HOWEVER, WERE NOT YET CONCLUDED...

SURRENDER YOUR CHARGE. WE ARE DELIVERERS OF THE COMMONWEALTH WHO EASE EVERY MAN OF HIS BURDEN.

YOU WOULD NOT EASE ME OF MINE COULD I BUT GIVE THREE STROKES IN ITS DEFENSE!

WE SHALL SEE THAT PRESENTLY. WHO IS THY MASTER?

HE IS KNOWN AS THE DISINHERITED KNIGHT.

HE WHOSE GOOD LANCE WON TODAY'S TOURNEY?

COMRADES! HE IS TOO LIKE OURSELVES TO MAKE BOOTY OF HIM.

LIKE US!? HOW?

FOOL! IS HE NOT POOR AS WE ARE? HATH HE NOT BEATEN THE NORMANS, AS WE WOULD IF WE COULD?

THOU MAYST GO THY WAYS, MY FRIEND. MY MEN WILL GUIDE THEE HOME SAFELY.

Day two of the games at Ashby--again attended by Isaac, Rebecca, Cedric, and Rowena--began with the general tournament in which all knights fought at once. The Disinherited Knight was the leader of one body, while Bois-Guilbert, rated as second best the previous day, was leader of the other.

THE TRUMPETS SOUNDED...

...AND BOTH PARTIES MET IN THE FIELD WITH A SHOCK HEARD A MILE'S DISTANCE.

FOR THE TEMPLE! FOR THE TEMPLE!

DESDICHADO! DESDICHADO!

Bois-Guilbert and the Disinherited Knight repeatedly tried to single out each other, spurred by mutual hatred, and aware that either's fall would be considered as decisive of victory.

When at last they met, Front-de-Boeuf and Athelstane--who had joined the Templar's team--found themselves free of attackers...

...AND DECIDED THEY WOULD BEST RENDER THEIR PARTY'S VICTORY BY AIDING THE TEMPLAR IN HIS CONTEST WITH HIS RIVAL.

II

SIR DISINHERITED KNIGHT, A SECOND TIME WE AWARDED TO YOU THE HONORS OF THIS TOURNEY.

RECEIVE FROM THE QUEEN OF LOVE AND BEAUTY THE CHAPLET OF HONOR WHICH YOUR VALOR HAS JUSTLY DESERVED.

HIS HEAD MUST BE BARE. THE MARSHALS MAY NOW REMOVE HIS HELMET.

THE KNIGHT MUTTERED A FEW FAINT WORDS AGAINST THIS ACTION, BUT THEY WERE EITHER LOST WITHIN THE HOLLOW OF HIS HELMET...

...OR IGNORED. TO THE ASTONISHMENT OF ALL, WILFRED OF IVANHOE, SON OF CEDRIC, STOOD REVEALED.

IVANHOE!

THE MARSHALS, GUESSING THE CAUSE OF HIS SWOON, HASTENED TO UNDO HIS ARMOR...

...AND FOUND THAT THE HEAD OF A LANCE HAD PENETRATED HIS SIDE.

UNABLE TO PUBLICLY ACKNOWLEDGE HIS DISOWNED SON, CEDRIC SENT HIS MEN TO CARE FOR HIM WHEN THE CROWD HAD DISPERSED.

WHEN THEY ARRIVED, HOWEVER, THE KNIGHT OF IVANHOE WAS NOWHERE TO BE SEEN.

THE ONLY INFORMATION THEY COULD COLLECT WAS THAT IVANHOE HAD BEEN RAISED BY WELL-ATTIRED MEN---

--AND PLACED IN THE CARE OF A LADY AMONG THE SPECTATORS.

THUS INFORMED THAT HIS SON WAS IN CAREFUL AND PROBABLY FRIENDLY HANDS, CEDRIC PLANNED TO RETURN THE FOLLOWING DAY.

WALDEMAR FITZURSE, RETURNING TO THE CASTLE OF ASHBY, MET WITH MAURICE DE BRACY, A KNIGHT IN PRINCE JOHN'S RETINUE.

WHAT MUMMERY IS THIS, DE BRACY? WHAT DOST THOU PROPOSE BY THIS DISGUISE?

TO GET ME A WIFE.

I COMPREHEND THEE NOT.

IN THIS SAME ATTIRE, FITZURSE, I WILL FALL UPON THE PARTY OF CEDRIC AND CARRY OFF THE LOVELY ROWENA.

ART THOU MAD, DE BRACY?

I THINK NOT. SEEM I NOT IN THIS GARB A BOLD OUTLAW? THE BLAME SHALL REST WITH THE THIEVES OF THE FORESTS.

WHEN NEXT DAY'S MARCH BRINGS CEDRIC'S PARTY WITHIN REACH WE WILL SWOOP ON THEM, CONDUCT HER TO FRONT-DE-BOEUF'S CASTLE--

--AND PRODUCE HER NOT AGAIN TO HER KINDRED UNTIL SHE BE THE BRIDE OF MAURICE DE BRACY.

A SAGE PLAN. WHO AIDED THEE IN ITS INVENTION?

BRIAN DE BOIS-GUILBERT. HE IS TO ASSIST ME AND HIS MEN WILL IMPERSONATE THE OUTLAWS.

BEFORE HIS RETURN TO ROTHERWOOD, CEDRIC CHANCED TO SEE GURTH, AND IMMEDIATELY HAD HIM BOUND AS A CAPTIVE.

HIS MIND, HOWEVER, WAS UPON OTHER MATTERS...

ROWENA, I WILL ASK YOU AGAIN--IN LIGHT OF WILFRED'S ABSENCE, WILT THOU CONSIDER MARRYING NOBLE ATHELSTANE?

FATHER...

MY HEART BELONGS TO WILFRED AND NO OTHER. AND WERE HE OUT OF THE QUESTION---

I WOULD RATHER TAKE REFUGE IN A CONVENT THAN SHARE A TH'RONE WITH THE SAXON NOBLE, WHOM I HAVE ALWAYS DESPISED AND HAVE RECENTLY BEGUN TO THOROUGHLY DETEST.

AS THEY JOURNEYED ON THEIR WAY, THEY WERE ALARMED BY CRIES FOR HELP. WHEN THEY LOCATED THE SOURCE, THEY FOUND ISAAC OF YORK, ABANDONED BY HIS GUARDS.

WOULD IT BUT PLEASE YOUR VALORS TO PERMIT THE POOR JEWS TO TRAVEL UNDER YOUR SAFEGUARD, I SWEAR YOUR FAVOR WILL BE GRATEFULLY ACKNOWLEDGED.

IT IS NOT FOR OURSELVES THAT WE ASK THIS. I BESEECH YOU, LET THIS SICK PERSON BE MOVED WITH CARE UNDER YOUR PROTECTION.

THE MAN IS OLD AND FEEBLE--THEIR FRIEND IN PERIL OF HIS LIFE. WE CANNOT LEAVE THEM.

I AGREE. THEY MAY JOIN US.

15

AMID THE BUSTLE, GURTH PREVAILED UPON THE JESTER TO SLACK THE CORD WHICH BOUND HIM.

WHEN THIS WAS DONE, GURTH FOUND NO DIFFICULTY IN FREEING HIS ARMS ALTOGETHER...

...AND, GLIDING INTO THE THICKET, MADE HIS ESCAPE.

IT WAS SOME TIME BEFORE HE WAS MISSED, AND BY THE TIME THEY REALIZED HE WAS GONE--

--THEY WERE ASSAILED IN FRONT, FLANK, AND REAR AT ONCE.

OF ALL THE PARTY, ONLY ONE ESCAPED.

THE JESTER WAMBA, AS SOON AS HE FOUND HIMSELF SAFE, HESITATED MORE THAN ONCE WHETHER HE SHOULD NOT TURN BACK AND SHARE THE CAPTIVITY OF A MASTER TO WHOM HE WAS SINCERELY ATTACHED.

I HAVE HEARD MEN TALK OF THE BLESSINGS OF FREEDOM...

...BUT I WISH A WISE MAN WOULD TELL ME WHAT USE TO MAKE OF IT NOW THAT I HAVE IT.

WAMBA!

GURTH!

WHAT IS THE MATTER? WHAT MEAN THESE CRIES AND CLASHINGS OF SWORDS?

MY LORD CEDRIC, MY LADY ROWENA AND ALL THEIR GROUP ARE PRISONERS.

IN THE NAME OF GOD! PRISONERS!? TO WHOM?

AY, WHO IS IT THAT RIFLE, RANSOM, AND MAKE PRISONERS IN THESE FORESTS?

YOU MAY LOOK CLOSE, AND SEE IF THEY BE THY FELLOW'S COATS, FOR THEY ARE LIKE THINE OWN AS ONE PEA-POD IS TO ANOTHER.

I WILL LEARN THAT PRESENTLY. STAY HERE UNTIL I RETURN.

SHALL WE STAND, GURTH? OR SHALL WE FLEE?

I HAVE EXPERIENCE THAT WARRANTS THESE THIEVES ARE NOT THE WORST MEN IN THE WORLD.

FRIEND GURTH, I HAVE LEARNT TO WHOM THE IMPOSTERS BELONG AND WHITHER THEY ARE BOUND.

FOR THREE MEN TO ATTEMPT A RESCUE WOULD BE MADNESS.

COME, THEN, I GATHER MORE AID.

AT THIS TIME, THE BLACK KNIGHT-- WHO HAD VANISHED FROM THE FIELD FOLLOWING IVANHOE'S VICTORY OVER BOIS-GUILBERT--FOUND HIMSELF FATIGUED FROM TRAVEL AND SOUGHT A PLACE TO SPEND THE NIGHT.

HOWEVER...

PASS ON, WHOSOEVER THOU ART, AND DISTURB NOT A SERVANT OF GOD IN HIS DEVOTIONS.

WORTHY FATHER, I AM A POOR WANDERER WHO GIVES THEE THE OPPORTUNITY OF EXERCISING THY HOSPITALITY.

I HAVE NOTHING HERE EVEN A DOG WOULD SHARE WITH ME. PASS THEN ON THY WAY, AND GOD SPEED THEE.

SIR HERMIT, THOU HAST NO RIGHT TO REFUSE SHELTER TO A WAYFARER IN DISTRESS.

OPEN THE DOOR OR I WILL BEAT IT DOWN.

PATIENCE THEN, GOOD TRAVELLER, AND SPARE THY STRENGTH. I WILL LET YOU IN.

ONCE INSIDE, THE BLACK KNIGHT FOUND THE HERMIT TO HAVE FOOD AND DRINK IN ABUNDANCE.

HOLY FATHER, PERMIT A SINFUL LAYMAN TO CRAVE THY NAME?

THOU MAYST CALL ME THE CLERK OF COPMANHURST. AND THOU?

IN THESE PARTS I AM CALLED THE BLACK KNIGHT.

SET THEE DOWN, THEN, AND FILL THY CUP. LET US DRINK, SING, AND MAKE MERRY.

18

Their reveries, however, were interrupted by a disturbance from without.

MAD PRIEST--OPEN TO LOCKSLEY!

WHY, HERMIT-- WHAT BOON COMPANION HAST THOU HERE?

A BROTHER OF OUR ORDER.

YOU CAN SPEAK TO NO ONE TO WHOM ENGLAND, AND THE LIVES OF HER PEOPLE, CAN BE DEARER THAN TO ME.

A BAND OF DISGUISED VILLAINS HAVE CAPTURED A PARTY OF NOBLE SAXONS AND TAKEN THEM TO A CASTLE IN THIS FOREST.

WILT THOU AID IN THEIR RESCUE?

I AM BOUND BY MY VOW TO DO SO.

COME THEN, WE MUST COLLECT WHAT FEW FORCES WE HAVE IF WE ARE TO STORM THE CASTLE OF REGINALD FRONT-DE-BŒUF.

WHAT!? IS IT FRONT-DE-BŒUF TURNED THIEF AND OPPRESSOR?

OPPRESSOR HE EVER WAS...

...AND I DOUBT IF EVER HE WERE HALF AS HONEST AS MANY A THIEF OF MY ACQUAINTANCE.

MEANWHILE, THE CAPTURED PARTY APPROACHED TORQUILSTONE, FRONT-DE-BOEUF'S CASTLE, FOR WHICH USE HE WOULD REQUIRE A SHARE OF SPOILS.

BOIS-GUILBERT FIXED ON THE LOVELY REBECCA AS HIS OWN PARTICULAR PRIZE--KNOWING THAT FRONT-DE-BOEUF HAD NO INTEREST IN A JEWESS.

ONCE INSIDE THE CASTLE, THE PRISONERS WERE SEPARATED...

...AND ISAAC WAS SOON VISITED BY FRONT-DE BOEUF HIMSELF.

ISSAC OF YORK, SEEST THOU THESE SCALES?

IN THESE THOU SHALT WEIGH ME OUT A THOUSAND SILVER POUNDS.

HOLY ABRAHAM! I HAVE NOT THE MEANS OF SATISFYING SUCH A DEMAND!

CHOOSE, JEW, BETWIXT A SCORCHING BED AND THE SILVER, FOR THOU HAST NO OTHER OPTION.

I...WILL PAY. LET MY DAUGHTER REBECCA GO FORTH TO YORK, AND THE SUM WILL BE YOURS.

THY DAUGHTER!? I HAD DEEMED HER THY CONCUBINE...

...AND HAVE GIVEN HER TO SIR BRIAN DE BOIS-GUILBERT.

ROBBER AND VILLAIN! I WILL PAY THEE NOTHING UNLESS SHE IS BROUGHT TO ME IN SAFETY AND HONOR!

WE SHALL SEE. STRIP HIM, SLAVES.

MEANWHILE, IN ANOTHER PART OF THE CASTLE...

PLEASE, PROUD DAMSEL, BE SEATED.

ALAS! FAIR ROWENA, YOU ARE IN THE PRESENCE OF YOUR CAPTIVE, NOT YOUR JAILER.

I KNOW YOU NOT, SIR...

IF I BE IN THE PRESENCE OF MY JAILER, SIR KNIGHT, IT BEST BECOMES A PRISONER TO REMAIN STANDING TILL SHE LEARNS HER DOOM.

...AND THE INSOLENT FAMILIARITY YOU APPLY TO ME IS NO APOLOGY FOR THE VIOLENCE OF A ROBBER.

I AM MAURICE DE BRACY, AND I TELL THEE, THOU SHALT NEVER LEAVE THIS CASTLE--

--OR THOU SHALT LEAVE IT AS MY WIFE.

SIR KNIGHT, WHEN I LEAVE, IT SHALL BE WITH ONE WHO HAS NOT LEARNT TO DESPISE THE MANNERS IN WHICH I WAS RAISED.

DREAM NOT THAT IVANHOE WILL EVER LEAD THEE AWAY. HE IS IN MY POWER WITHIN THIS CASTLE.

WILFRED? HERE?! SAVE HIM, FOR THE LOVE OF HEAVEN!

IT IS THY LOVE THAT MUST BUY HIS PROTECTION, AND CEDRIC'S ALSO.

CEDRIC! MY GUARDIAN! I DESERVE THIS EVIL FOR FORGETTING HIS FATE EVEN IN THAT OF HIS SON!

ROWENA'S TEARS FLOWED...

...AND SOFTENED DE BRACY'S HEART, WHO COULD NOT LOOK ON SO FAIR A FACE WHILE DISTURBED WITH AGONY.

21

AND IN A ROOM HIGH IN A SECLUDED, INESCAPABLE TOWER...

TAKE THESE, GOOD FRIEND, AND FOR GOD'S SAKE BE MERCIFUL TO US!

FAIR FLOWER OF PALESTINE, I HAVE MADE A VOW TO PREFER BEAUTY TO WEALTH.

THOU ART NO OUTLAW, THEN. THOU ART A NORMAN, NOBLE PERHAPS IN BIRTH.

O, BE SO NOW AND CAST OFF THIS MASK OF OUTRAGE AND VIOLENCE!

I AM ONE WHO WOULD RATHER GIVE THEE PEARLS AND DIAMONDS, THAN DEPRIVE THEE OF THEM.

THEN WHAT WOULDST THOU HAVE OF ME? YOU ARE A CHRISTIAN, I A JEWESS.

OUR UNION WERE CONTRARY TO THE LAWS ALIKE OF CHURCH AND SYNAGOGUE.

INDEED. WED WITH A JEWESS! DESPARDIEUX! I AM A TEMPLAR. BEHOLD THE CROSS OF MY HOLY ORDER.

AND SO, ONLY ONE THING CAN SAVE THEE, REBECCA. SUBMIT TO THY FATE, AND EMBRACE OUR RELIGION.

AND WHAT RELIGION CAN IT BE THAT HARBORS SUCH A VILLAIN!? CRAVEN KNIGHT--FORESWORN PRIEST! I SPIT AT THEE, AND I DEFY THEE!

REMAIN WHERE THOU ART, TEMPLAR, OR AT THY CHOICE ADVANCE! ONE FOOT NEARER AND I PLUNGE MYSELF FROM THE PRECIPICE--

--MY BODY SHALL BE CRUSHED, ERE IT BECOME THE VICTIM OF THY BRUTALITY.

YOU DO ME INJUSTICE. I WILL DO THEE NO INJURY WHATSOEVER.

IF NOT FOR THYSELF, FOR THY FATHER'S SAKE FORBEAR! I WILL BE HIS FRIEND, AND IN THIS CASTLE HE WILL NEED A POWERFUL ONE.

COME DOWN, RASH GIRL! I SWEAR BY EARTH, SEA, AND SKY I WILL OFFER THEE NO OFFENSE.

I WILL NOT TRUST THEE, TEMPLAR.

ALAS! DARE I TRUST THEE?

PEACE, BUT WITH THIS SPACE BETWEEN US.

THOU DOST ME INJUSTICE!

MANY A LAW AND A COMMANDMENT HAVE I BROKEN, BUT MY WORD--*NEVER.*

LET THERE BE PEACE BETWEEN US, REBECCA.

AT THAT MOMENT, THE SOUND OF A BUGLE THRICE WINDED WITHOUT THE CASTLE.

VOICES CALLED FOR FRONT-DE-BOEUF, LEAVING THE JEW TO THANK GOD FOR HIS DELIVERANCE...

ELSEWHERE, MAURICE DE BRACY, HEARD IT AS WELL...

THAT BUGLE ANNOUNCES SOMETHING WHICH MAY REQUIRE MY ATTENTION.

I WILL SOON RETURN AND HOLD FURTHER CONFERENCE WITH THEE.

...AND OF THEM ALL, PERHAPS, HE LEAST REGRETTED THE INTERRUPTION.

24

IT WAS FRONT-DE-BOEUF'S OWN PLAN, HOWEVER, TO SEND THE PRIEST BACK WITH A PLEA FOR AID TO BE DELIVERED TO HIS ALLIES.

THE JESTER SWITCHED CLOTHES WITH CEDRIC, WHO WAS GIVEN THE LETTER AS HE LEFT THE CASTLE--

--A LETTER THAT WOULD NEVER BE DELIVERED.

WAMBA'S SHARP WIT AND TONGUE SOON LED TO HIS DISCOVERY...

GO AND FETCH ME THE RIGHT CEDRIC HITHER. I PARDON YOUR ERROR--YOU BUT MISTOOK A FOOL FOR A SAXON FRANKLIN.

YOUR EXCELLENCY WILL FIND THERE ARE MORE FOOLS THAN FRANKLINS AMONG US.

WHAT MEANS THE KNAVE?

FIENDS OF HELL! HE MUST HAVE ESCAPED IN THE MONK'S GARMENTS! WHAT HAVE WE TO EXPECT BUT INSTANT STORM?

TO THE BATTLEMENTS, THEN! LET US MARK WHAT THEY DO WITHOUT.

BY MY FAITH, THESE MEN APPROACH WITH MORE DISCIPLINE THAN EXPECTED.

THEY MUST BE LED BY ONE SKILLFUL IN THE PRACTICE OF WARS.

I ESPY HIM.

THE BLACK KNIGHT, WHO OVERTHREW THEE AT ASHBY.

I SHOULD IN VAIN HAVE SOUGHT FOR HIM. SO MUCH THE BETTER THAT HE COMES HERE TO GIVE ME MY REVENGE!

25

THE IMMEDIATE ATTACK CUT OFF ALL FURTHER TALK. EACH KNIGHT REPAIRED TO HIS POST AS THE STORMING OF TORQUILSTONE BEGAN.

ELSEWHERE IN THE CASTLE, REBECCA, FREED FROM CAPTIVITY DURING THE CHAOS, SOUGHT AND FOUND THE WOUNDED INVANHOE.

SHE HAD INDEED BEEN HEEDFULLY RAISED IN ALL THE KNOWLEDGE PROPER TO HER NATION. HER MASTERY OF MEDICINE HAD BEEN ACQUIRED UNDER AN AGED JEWESS NAMED MIRIAM...

...WHOSE FATE HAD BEEN TO FALL TO THE FANATICISM OF THE TIME-- BUT HER SECRETS HAD SURVIVED IN HER APT PUPIL.

WHEN IVANHOE REACHED ISAAC'S HABITATION FOLLOWING HIS COLLAPSE UPON THE LISTS, REBECCA HAD EXAMINED THE WOUND...

...AND, AFTER APPLYING THE HEALING BALSAM OF MIRIAM, KNEW THERE WAS NOTHING TO FEAR HIS LIFE.

SHE KNEW ALSO THAT THERE WAS NO REMEDY FOR HER GROWING AFFECTION TOWARD HIM.

IF I COULD BUT DRAG MYSELF TO YONDER WINDOW, THAT I MIGHT SEE HOW THIS BRAVE GAME IS LIKE TO GO!

I MYSELF WILL STAND AT THE LATTICE, AND DESCRIBE TO YOU WHAT PASSES WITHOUT.

"HOLY PROPHETS OF THE LAW! FRONT-DE-BOEUF AND THE BLACK KNIGHT FIGHT HAND TO HAND.

"THE BLACK KNIGHT IS DOWN! HIS SWORD IS BROKEN...!"

"...BUT HE REGAINS A WEAPON! HE FIGHTS AS IF THERE WERE TWENTY MEN'S STRENGTH IN HIS SINGLE ARM.

"THE UNITED FORCE OF THE ENEMY GIVES THE CHAMPION PAUSE AS FRONT-DE-BOEUF, MORTALLY WOUNDED, IS BROUGHT WITHIN THE CASTLE.

"THE ASSAILANTS SOON FALL BEFORE HIM, AND HE APPROACHES THE POSTERN GATE.

"THE THUNDERING BLOWS HE DEALS-YOU MAY HEAR THEM ABOVE ALL THE DIN AND SHOUTS OF THE BATTLE.

"THE GATE FALLS!"

THE BLACK KNIGHT QUICKLY ORDERED THE CONSTRUCTION OF A FLOATING BRIDGE, AND LED HIS FOLLOWERS ACROSS THE MOAT.

BUT ONCE INSIDE THEY FOUND THE BRIDGE WHICH COMMUNICATES WITH THE CASTLE DESTROYED BY BOIS-GUILBERT.

REBECCA RELATED ALL THESE EVENTS IN FAITHFUL DETAIL TO IVANHOE...

I WOULD ENDURE TEN YEARS' CAPTIVITY TO FIGHT ONE DAY BY THAT GOOD KNIGHT'S SIDE IN A QUARREL SUCH AS THIS!

HOW COULDST THOU HOPE TO INFLICT WOUNDS ON OTHERS ERE THINE OWN BE HEALED?

THOU KNOWEST NOT HOW IMPOSSIBLE IT IS FOR ONE TRAINED TO ACTIONS OF CHIVALRY TO REMAIN PASSIVE...

...WHEN OTHERS ACT DEEDS OF HONOR AROUND HIM.

ALAS! WHAT REMAINS TO YOU AS THE PRIZE OF ALL THE BLOOD YOU HAVE SPILLED?

WHAT REMAINS? GLORY, MAIDEN-- GLORY!

GLORY!? IS THE RUSTED MAIL WHICH HANGS OVER THE CHAMPION'S MOULDERING TOMB SUFFICIENT REWARD FOR A LIFE SPENT MISERABLY THAT YE MAKE OTHERS MISERABLE?

THOU WOULDST QUENCH THE LIGHT OF CHIVALRY WHICH ALONE DISTINGUISHES THE NOBLE FROM THE BASE.

I...I...

WELL THOU HAST SPOKEN, SIR KNIGHT. IT ILL BESEEMETH THE JEWISH DAMSEL TO SPEAK OF BATTLE OR WAR.

THIS SHE SPOKE IN A TONE OF SORROW, EMBITTERED BY THE IDEA THAT IVANHOE CONSIDERED HER AS ONE NOT ENTITLED TO INTERFERE IN A CASE OF HONOR.

HE SLEEPS. ALAS! IS IT A CRIME THAT I SHOULD LOOK UPON HIM WHEN IT MAY BE FOR THE LAST TIME?

AND WITH THOSE WORDS SHE FORTIFIED, OR ENDEAVORED TO FORTIFY, HER MIND, NOT ONLY AGAINST THE EVILS FROM WITHOUT...

...BUT ALSO AGAINST TREACHEROUS FEELINGS WHICH ASSAILED HER FROM WITHIN.

MERRY ST. GEORGE FOR ENGLAND! TO THE *CHARGE*, BOLD YEOMEN! SEE YONDER FLAMES?

ONE EFFORT, AND TORQUILSTONE IS *OURS!*

THE CASTLE BURNS BEHIND US VILLAINS! LET DESPAIR GIVE YOU COURAGE...

...OR LET ME FORWARD! I WILL COPE WITH THIS CHAMPION MYSELF!

THE PASSAGE RANG WITH THE FURIOUS BLOWS THEY DEALT EACH OTHER...

YIELD THEE, DE BRACY.

I WILL NOT YIELD TO AN UNKNOWN CONQUEROR.

THE BLACK KNIGHT WHISPERED INTO HIS EAR, AND INSTANTLY CHANGED DE BRACY'S TONE TO SULLEN SUBMISSION.

I YIELD ME TO BE TRUE PRISONER.

GO TO YONDER TOWER, AND THERE WAIT MY FURTHER ORDERS.

FIRST LET ME SAY THIS. WILFRED OF IVANHOE IS WOUNDED AND A PRISONER, AND WILL PERISH WITHOUT PRESENT HELP.

IVANHOE!? SHOW ME HIS CHAMBER, DE BRACY!

THE CASTLE *BURNS!* WHAT CAN WE DO TO *SAVE* OURSELVES?

FLY, REBECCA, AND SAVE THINE *OWN* LIFE.

I WILL *NOT*. WE WILL BE SAVED OR PERISH *TOGETHER*.

I HAVE FOUND THEE, REBECCA. UP, AND INSTANTLY FOLLOW ME!

BOIS-GUILBERT, RATHER WILL I PERISH THAN ACCEPT SAFETY FROM THEE!

THOU SHALT NOT CHOOSE. ONCE DIDST THOU FOIL ME, BUT NEVER MORTAL DID SO TWICE.

HOUND OF THE TEMPLE! SET *FREE* THE DAMSEL! VILLAIN, I WILL HAVE THY *HEART'S BLOOD!*

I HAD NOT FOUND THEE, WILFORD, BUT FOR THY SHOUTS.

THINK NOT OF ME! PURSUE YON RAVISHER--SAVE THE LADY ROWENA--LOOK TO THE NOBLE CEDRIC!

IN THEIR TURN-- BUT THINE IS FIRST.

OUTSIDE, THE TEMPLAR FLED WITH HIS PRIZE. ATHELSTANE ATTEMPED TO STOP HIM, BUT BOIS-GUILBERT DEALT HIM A FEARFUL BLOW THAT LEVELLED HIM TO THE EARTH.

SOON AFTER, LOCKSLEY'S VOICE WAS HEARD TO SHOUT THAT THE DEN OF TYRANTS WAS NO MORE.

MORNING. ALL WERE GATHERED UNDER THE TRYSTING-TREE WHERE THEY HAD SPENT THE NIGHT RESTING AFTER THE SIEGE.

ALL, THAT IS, EXCEPT ISAAC AND THE CLERK OF COPMANHURST, WHO HAD YET TO BE FOUND.

GOOD YEOMAN, MY HEART IS OPPRESSED WITH SADNESS. NOBLE ATHELSTANE IS NO MORE.

MY PEOPLE DO BUT TARRY MY PRESENCE TO TAKE HIS REMAINS TO THEIR LAST MANSION. I WAITED BUT TO RENDER MY THANKS.

TAKE OF THE SPOIL WHAT MAY REWARD THEM.

I AM RICH ENOUGH TO USE MINE OWN WEALTH.

BUT THOU--HOW SHALL I REWARD THEE WHO FEARED NOT TO GIVE THY BODY TO CHAINS AND DEATH INSTEAD OF MINE?

IF YOU WOULD PLEASURE ME, I PRAY YOU TO PARDON GURTH.

I WILL BOTH PARDON HIM *AND* REWARD HIM WITH HIS FREEDOM.

SIR KNIGHT, A HOME IS SOMETIMES DESIRABLE EVEN TO ONE WHOSE TRADE IS WANDERING.

THOU HAST EARNED ONE IN ROTHERWOOD.

THERE I WILL COME, BRAVE SAXON...

BUT, AS NOW MATTERS DETAIN ME FROM YOUR HALLS.

WHEN I DO COME HITHER, I WILL ASK A BOON AS WILL PUT THY GENEROSITY TO THE TEST.

IT IS GRANTED ALREADY.

DURING THE FUNERAL OF ATHELSTANE, I WILL STAY IN HIS CASTLE OF CONINGSBURGH. PEACE.

GOD SPEED THEE, NOBLE KNIGHT.

DE BRACY, THOU ARE FREE AS WELL. DEPART.

DE BRACY WITHDREW, THREW HIMSELF INTO THE SADDLE, AND GALLOPED OFF THROUGH THE WOOD.

NOBLE KNIGHT, I WILL PRAY YOU TO KEEP THIS AS A MEMORIAL.

AND IF YE CHANCE TO BE HARD BESTED IN THESE FORESTS, WIND THREE MOTS AND YE SHALL FIND HELPERS AND RESCUE.

I WOULD WE COULD HEAR TIDINGS OF OUR JOYOUS CHAPLAIN--

MAKE ROOM, MY MERRY MEN!

MAD PRIEST! WHOM HAST THOU GOT THERE?

ALAS! I AM AN AGED BEGGAR'D MAN--AND I FEAR ME A CHILDLESS ONE.

WAS NOT THY DAUGHTER DARK-HAIRED, AND WORE SHE NOT A VEIL BROIDERED WITH SILVER?

SHE WAS, AND SHE DID! CANST THOU TELL ME AUGHT OF HER SAFETY!

IT WAS SHE, THEN, I SAW CARRIED OFF BY THE PROUD TEMPLAR AND TAKEN, NO DOUBT, TO THE PRECEPTORY OF TEMPLESTOWE.

O REBECCA, DAUGHTER OF MY BELOVED RACHAEL! WHAT CAN I DO?

PERHAPS PRIOR AYMSLEY WILL AGREE TO USE HIS INFLUENCE WITH THE TEMPLAR AND WRITE A LETTER GIVING YOU SAFE CONDUCT THERE.

THIS WAS DONE, AND WHEN ISAAC HAD DEPARTED THE BLACK KNIGHT TOOK HIS LEAVE AS WELL, WITH WAMBA THE GUIDE TO HIS NEXT DESTINATION.

THIS WAS THE PRIORY OF ST. BOTOLPH, TO WHICH IVANHOE HAD BEEN MOVED WHEN THE CASTLE WAS TAKEN.

THOU WILT MEET ME AT CONINGSBURGH, AND IT WILL BE MY TASK TO RECONCILE THEE TO THY FATHER.

I AM ANXIOUS TO ATTEND THEE, SIR KNIGHT.

REST THIS DAY, WILFRED. THOU WILT HAVE SCARCE STRENGTH TO TRAVEL ON THE NEXT.

FARE THEE WELL. I CHARGE THEE NOT TO ATTEMPT TRAVEL TILL TOMORROW AT EARLIEST.

IVANHOE, THOUGH HE SAID NOTHING TO THE BLACK KNIGHT, FELT HIMSELF STOUT ENOUGH TO TRADE BUFFETS WITH ANY CHALLENGER...

...AND IMMEDIATELY BEGAN PREPARING FOR HIS DEPARTURE.

MEANWHILE, AT THE CASTLE OF YORK, DE BRACY HAS TOLD PRINCE JOHN THE FATES OF FRONT-DE-BOEUF AND THE TEMPLAR...

THE WORST NEWS IS NOT YET SAID. RICHARD IS IN ENGLAND. I HAVE SEEN AND SPOKEN WITH HIM.

THOU RAVEST. IT CANNOT BE.

IT IS AS TRUE AS TRUTH ITSELF. I WAS HIS PRISONER.

HE IS THEN AT THE HEAD OF A POWER?

ONLY A FEW OUTLAWS WERE AROUND HIM, FITZURSE, AND HE SAID HE WAS ABOUT TO DEPART FROM THEM.

IF THIS OBJECT OF OUR TERROR JOURNEYS ALONE, HE MUST BE MET WITHAL.

NOT BY ME--HE TOOK ME TO MERCY. I WILL NOT HARM HIM.

WHO SPOKE OF HARMING HIM? NO--A PRISON WERE BETTER, AND WHETHER IN BRITAIN OR AUSTRIA, WHAT MATTERS IT?

33

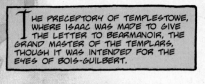

THE PRECEPTORY OF TEMPLESTOWE, WHERE ISAAC WAS MADE TO GIVE THE LETTER TO BEARMANOIR, THE GRAND MASTER OF THE TEMPLARS, THOUGH IT WAS INTENDED FOR THE EYES OF BOIS-GUILBERT.

WHAT MEANETH HE BY THIS? THIS REBECCA OF YORK WAS A PUPIL OF THAT MIRIAM OF WHOM I HAVE HEARD?

"...THOU HAST ESCAPED WITH THAT FAIR JEWISH SORCERESS WHOSE BLACK EYES HAVE BEWITCHED THEE. WE PRAY THEE TO BE ON THY GUARD WITH THIS SECOND WITCH OF ENDOR--FOR YOUR GREAT MASTER COMES TO DIMINISH YOUR MIRTH."

AYE, GRACIOUS SIR, AND MANY A KNIGHT AND YEOMAN CAN TESTIFY THAT MY DAUGHTER HATH HEALED THEM BY HER ART.

MIRIAM---HER BODY WAS *BURNT* AT A STAKE AND HER ASHES *SCATTERED* TO THE FOUR WINDS.

AND SO BE IT WITH ME AND MINE ORDER, IF I DO NOT DO AS MUCH TO HER PUPIL!

BURN!?! MALVOISIN, SHE SHALL *NOT*, BY HEAVEN.

BY HEAVEN, SHE *MUST* AND *WILL!* NO ONE CAN SAVE HER!

ALBERT, THOU MUST CONNIVE AT HER ESCAPE.' I WILL TRANSPORT--

I CANNOT IF I WOULD. *THINK*, BRIAN. SHOULDST THOU ADHERE TO THY PASSION FOR REBECCA, BEAUMANOIR WILL NOT NEGLECT TO EXPEL THEE. WOMEN ARE BUT THE TOYS WHICH AMUSE OUR LIGHTER HOURS; *AMBITION* IS THE SERIOUS BUSINESS OF LIFE.

ARE THERE GROUNDS ENOUGH TO CONDEMN HER? WILL NOT THE GRAND MASTER CHANGE HIS MIND WHEN HE SEES THAT THE PROOFS ARE SO WEAK?

THEY MUST BE *STRENGTHENED*, COMRADE.

DOST THOU UNDERSTAND ME?

ELSEWHERE...

IF I MISTAKE NOT, THERE ARE COMPANY IN YONDER BRAKE THAT ARE ON THE LOOKOUT FOR US.

WHAT MAKES THEE JUDGE SO?

DIE, TYRANT!

HA! HAVE WE *TRAITORS* HERE?

TRUE TO HIS WORD, LOCKSLEY AND HIS MEN RESPONDED TO THE HORN AND THE ATTACK WAS FOILED.

WHEN ASKED WHO SENT HIM ON SUCH A TRAITOROUS DEED, FITZURSE RESPONDED--

THY FATHER'S SON.

LET THIS KNIGHT HAVE A STEED, LOCKSLEY, AND LET HIM DEPART UNHARMED.

I JUDGE I LISTEN TO A VOICE WHOSE BEHESTS MUST NOT BE DISPUTED.

THOU BEAREST AN ENGLISH HEART, AND JUDGE WELL THOU ART THE MORE BOUND TO OBEY ME. I AM RICHARD OF ENGLAND!

BRAVE LOCKSLEY--

CALL ME LOCKSLEY NO LONGER, MY LIEGE. I AM ROBIN HOOD OF SHERWOOD FOREST.

35

THE HALL WAS QUICKLY PREPARED FOR REBECCA'S TRIAL--FOR, AS MALVOISIN SAID TO BOIS-GUILBERT--

"...TRIAL MOVES RAPIDLY ON WHEN THE JUDGE HAS DETERMINED THE SENTENCE BEFOREHAND."

MY BRETHREN AND MY CHILDREN...WE HAVE SUMMONED INTO OUR PRESENCE A JEWISH WOMAN, REBECCA--A WOMAN FAMOUS FOR WITCHERIES--

--WHEREBY SHE HATH MADDENED THE BLOOD AND BESOTTED THE BRAIN OF A KNIGHT DEVOTED TO THE SERVICE OF THE HOLY TEMPLE.

"OUR BROTHER BRIAN IS WELL KNOWN TO OURSELVES, AND IF WE ARE TOLD THAT SUCH A MAN...

"...SUDDENLY CASTING AWAY REGARD FOR HIS VOWS AND BRETHREN, HAD ASSOCIATED HIMSELF WITH A JEWISH DAMSEL--"

--AND DEFENDED HER PERSON IN PREFERENCE TO HIS OWN, WHAT SHOULD WE SAY BUT THAT HE WAS INFLUENCED BY SOME WICKED SPELL?

IF BY THIS MEANS, SATAN HAD OBTAINED DOMINION OVER THE KNIGHT, OUR JUSTICE MAY BE SATISFIED..

...WITH THE PUNISHMENT OF THIS INFIDEL WOMAN.

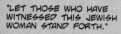

"LET THOSE WHO HAVE WITNESSED THIS JEWISH WOMAN STAND FORTH."

THE FIRST--HIGG, SON OF SNELL--TOLD HOW REBECCA'S BALSAM HAD ALLOWED HIM TO AGAIN WALK.

ANOTHER--A SOLDIER-- CLAIMED SHE HAD CURED A MAN'S WOUND BY MAKING SIGNS UPON IT AND REPEATING MYSTERIOUS WORDS.

THE FINAL SEALED HER FATE, FOR HE CLAIMED HE HAD SEEN REBECCA PERCH HERSELF ATOP THE TOWER...

...AND THERE TAKE THE FORM OF A MILK-WHITE SWAN, CIRCLE THE CASTLE THREE TIMES, AND RETURN TO ASSUME FEMALE FORM.

37

WILFRED OF IVANHOE ARRIVED SHORTLY AFTER RICHARD'S RESCUE, AND HIS ASTONISHMENT WAS BEYOND BOUNDS WHEN HE SAW HIS MASTER.

WILFRED!

TREASON HATH BEEN WITH US, IVANHOE. BUT NOW I BETHINK ME, THOU TOO ART A TRAITOR.

WHAT MEAN THESE MARKS OF DEATH AND DANGER, AND THE BLOODY ARMOR OF MY PRINCE?

WERE NOT MY ORDERS POSITIVE THAT THOU SHOULDST REPOSE THYSELF UNTIL THY WOUND WAS HEALED?

IT IS HEALED--AND IS NOT OF MORE CONCERN THAN THE SCRATCH OF A BODKIN.

THE PARTY RESUMED THEIR JOURNEY TO CONINGSBURGH CASTLE AND ARRIVED WITHOUT INTERRUPTION...

...AND THEY SOON STOOD IN THE HALL PREPARED FOR THE FUNERAL OF NOBLE ATHELSTANE.

I REMIND YOU, NOBLE CEDRIC, THAT WHEN WE PARTED YOU PROMISED TO GRANT ME A BOON.

IT IS GRANTED ERE NAMED, NOBLE KNIGHT. I TRUST IT REGARDS YOU AND NO OTHER...

IT DOES. AS YET YOU HAVE KNOWN ME AS THE BLACK KNIGHT--

--KNOW ME NOW AS RICHARD OF ENGLAND.

RICHARD!

AND NOW TO MY BOON. I REQUIRE OF THEE, AS A MAN OF THY WORD--

--TO FORGIVE THE GOOD KNIGHT WILFRED OF IVANHOE.

MY FATHER! GRANT ME THY FORGIVENESS!

THOU HAST IT, MY SON.

FATHER--

I CAN GUESS THE TOPIC OF THY WORDS. THE LADY ROWENA MUST COMPLETE TWO YEARS MOURNING, AS FOR A BETROTHED HUSBAND--

--OUR ANCESTORS WOULD DISOWN US WERE WE TO TREAT OF A NEW UNION ERE THE GRAVE OF HIM IS YET CLOSED.

THE GHOST OF ATHELSTANE HIMSELF WOULD STAND BEFORE US TO FORBID SUCH DISHONOR TO HIS MEN--

IN THE NAME OF GOD! ATHELSTANE!

IF THOU ART MORTAL, SPEAK! IF A DEPARTED SPIRIT, SAY WHY THOU DOST REVISIT US.

LIVING OR DEAD, NOBLE ATHELSTANE, SPEAK TO CEDRIC!

I AM ALIVE, FATHER CEDRIC.

ATHELSTANE, I MYSELF SAW YOU STRUCK DOWN BY THE FIERCE TEMPLAR.

AND I THOUGHT, AS WAMBA REPORTED, YOUR SKULL WAS CLOVEN THROUGH THE TEETH.

MY TEETH ARE IN GOOD ORDER, NO THANKS TO THE TEMPLAR--

--WHOSE SWORD TURNED IN HIS HAND SO THAT THE BLADE STRUCK ME FLATLINGS.

MY STEEL CAP HAD BEEN ON, BUT AS IT WAS I WENT DOWN STUNNED BUT UNWOUNDED.

I NEVER RECOVERED MY SENSES UNTIL I FOUND MYSELF IN A COFFIN--AN OPEN ONE BY GOOD LUCK!

MY WARD ROWENA-- I TRUST YOU INTEND NOT TO DESERT HER?

FATHER CEDRIC, BE REASONABLE. ROWENA LOVES WILFRED.

LEND ME THY HAND, ROWENA.

WILFRED OF IVANHOE, IN THY FAVOR I RENOUNCE--BY SAINT DUNSTAN! OUR COUSIN WILFRED HATH VANISHED!

THE LISTS OF ST. GEORGE-- CHOSEN BY THE GRAND MASTER AS THE PLACE OF COMBAT.

HERE STANDETH THE GOOD KNIGHT, SIR BRIAN, READY TO BATTLE ANY KNIGHT WHO WILL SUSTAIN THE QUARREL ALLOWED TO THE JEWESS REBECCA.

LET THE TRUMPETS SOUND...

HOURS PASSED...

IT BEGAN TO BE WHISPERED IT WAS TIME TO DECLARE REBECCA'S PLEDGE FORFEITED...

A CHAMPION! A CHAMPION!

I COME HITHER WITH LANCE AND SWORD TO UPHOLD THE DOOM PRONOUNCED AGAINST REBECCA TO BE FALSE AND TRUTHLESS.

I WILL NOT FIGHT THEE AT PRESENT.

A CHAMPION--BUT ONE WHOSE HORSE REELED FROM FATIGUE, AND WHO HIMSELF SEEMED SCARCE ABLE TO SUPPORT HIMSELF IN THE SADDLE.

GET THY WOUNDS HEALED AND PURVEY THEE A BETTER HORSE.

I WILL PROCLAIM THEE A COWARD, TEMPLAR, UNLESS THOU DO BATTLE WITHOUT FURTHER DELAY.

41

42

WHEN HIS HELMET WAS REMOVED, IT WAS FOUND THAT HE HAD DIED--

--A VICTIM TO THE VIOLENCE OF HIS OWN CONTENDING PASSIONS.

THIS IS INDEED THE JUDGMENT OF GOD!

I PRONOUNCE THE MAIDEN *FREE* AND *GUILTLESS!*

MANFULLY AND RIGHTFULLY HATH IT BEEN DONE. THE ARMS AND BODY OF THE DECEASED KNIGHT ARE AT THE WILL OF THE VICTOR.

I WILL NOT DESPOIL HIM OF WEAPONS, NOR CONDEMN HIS CORPSE TO SHAME.

HE HATH FOUGHT FOR CHRISTENDOM. GOD'S ARM, NO HUMAN HAND, HATH THIS DAY STRUCK HIM DOWN.

THE NUPTIALS OF IVANHOE, FORMALLY APPROVED BY HIS FATHER, WERE CELEBRATED IN YORK. KING RICHARD HIMSELF ATTENDED.

THE UNION WAS CELEBRATED BY NORMANS AS WELL AS SAXONS, WHO MARKED IT AS A PLEDGE OF FUTURE PEACE AND HARMONY BETWEEN THE TWO RACES.

43

UPON THE SECOND MORNING AFTER THIS HAPPY BRIDAL, ROWENA RECEIVED AN UNEXPECTED VISITOR.

WHAT MEANS THIS, LADY? OR WHY DO YOU OFFER ME A DEFERENCE SO UNUSUAL?

BECAUSE OF YOU, LADY, I MAY LAWFULLY PAY THE DEBT OF GRATITUDE WHICH I OWE TO WILFRED OF IVANHOE.

I AM THE UNHAPPY JEWESS FOR WHOM YOUR HUSBAND HAZARDED HIS LIFE.

DAMSEL, WILFRED ON THAT DAY RENDERED BACK BUT IN SLIGHT MEASURE YOUR CHARITY TOWARDS HIM IN HIS WOUNDS AND MISFORTUNES.

IS THERE AUGHT REMAINS IN WHICH HE OR I CAN SERVE THEE?

NOTHING--UNLESS YOU WILL TRANSMIT TO HIM MY GRATEFUL FAREWELL.

YOU LEAVE ENGLAND, THEN?

I LEAVE IT ERE THIS MOON AGAIN CHANGES. AMONG OUR PEOPLE HAVE BEEN WOMEN WHO HAVE DEVOTED THEIR LIVES TO TENDING THE SICK AND FEEDING THE HUNGRY.

AMONG THESE WILL REBECCA BE NUMBERED.

FAREWELL. MAY HE WHO MADE BOTH JEW AND CHRISTIAN SHOWER ON YOU HIS BLESSINGS.

IVANHOE DISTINGUISHED HIMSELF IN RICHARD'S SERVICE AND GAINED MARKS OF ROYAL FAVOR. HE MIGHT HAVE RISEN HIGHER STILL BUT FOR THE KING'S PREMATURE DEATH.

WITH ROWENA, IVANHOE LIVED LONG AND HAPPILY, FOR THEY WERE ATTACHED TO EACH OTHER BY THE BONDS OF EARLY AFFECTION, AND THEY LOVED EACH OTHER THE MORE FROM THE RECOLLECTION OF THE OBSTACLES THAT IMPEDED THEIR UNION.

The End

Sir Walter Scott was born in 1771 in Edinburgh, Scotland, the son of a lawyer and writer to the Signet. He could trace his ancestry to famous families on the Scottish side of the border with England, and this led him early on to develop a love of border history. He became a romantic antiquarian, an interest that was fed by the ballads, fairy tales, and romances he read voraciously; by the folk tales he heard from peasants in his travels; and by the romantic poetry, from France, Italy, and Germany, he admired. Scott graduated from Edinburgh University, where he studied law, and was admitted to the bar in 1792. His literary career began in 1796 with an anonymously published translation of the ballads of G.A. Bürger, a contemporary German poet. He followed this effort with a translation of Goethe, and with other similar works, before the publication of Coleridge's *Christabel* inspired him to write poems. These poems, he hoped, would do for the Scottish border what the Germans' had done for their middle ages: make the past live again in modern romances. Narrative poems such as *The Lay of the Last Minstrel* (1805), *Marmion* (1808), and *The Lady of the Lake* (1810) made him famous. During this period he also wrote reviews, edited several historical works, established the Tory-oriented *Quarterly Review*, and had interests in several printing and publishing agreements. Feeling eclipsed as a poet by Byron, Scott turned to the novels that have brought him lasting recognition. His first, *Waverly* (1814), was followed by a horde of others published over the next ten years, among them *Rob Roy* (1817), *Ivanhoe* (1819), *Kenilworth* (1821), and *The Talisman* (1825). He continued to edit, adapt, and review other works; practice law; and entertain on a grand scale at Abbotsford, his estate. Not surprisingly, his health suffered, and at one point he almost died. When, in 1826, he found himself greatly in debt after a financial crisis involving his publisher and his printing interests, he set to work writing at a furious pace in an attempt to pay off his obligations. He almost succeeded, but his health was still impaired, and he couldn't take the strain for long. Scott died in 1832.

Ray Lago was born in Jersey City, New Jersey, in 1958. After graduating from Kean College in 1981, he worked as an advertising artist for Continuity Associates, a commercial art company owned by noted illustrator Neal Adams. As a freelancer, Lago has illustrated for such clients as *Reader's Digest,* Doubleday & Co., Letraset, and *Scholastic Magazine;* his work received a number of awards, including a Desi Award for Excellence and a Certificate of Excellence from the Art Director's Club of New Jersey. Lago's freelance stints were interrupted by employment as a video paintbox illustrator for NBC News, the "Today Show," ABC News, ABC Sports, and PBS's "The MacNeil Lehrer News Hour." In 1989, Lago abandoned the broadcast industry for the comics field. His credits include three volumes of *Open Space.*

Mark Wayne Harris was born in New Jersey in 1964. At the age of 19, he made his first writing sale to a comic book publisher. Harris soon moved to Blackthorne Publishing, where he wrote *MerlinRealm,* the critically acclaimed *Street Wolf,* and the controversial *Danse. Ivanhoe* marks his return to illustrated fiction, after a three-year absence to pursue other writing projects.

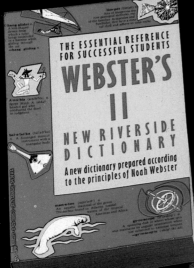
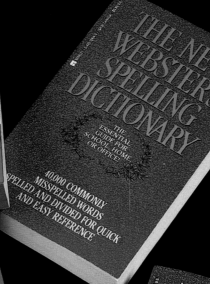
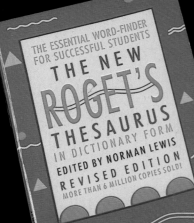